How many?

2

How many?

How many?

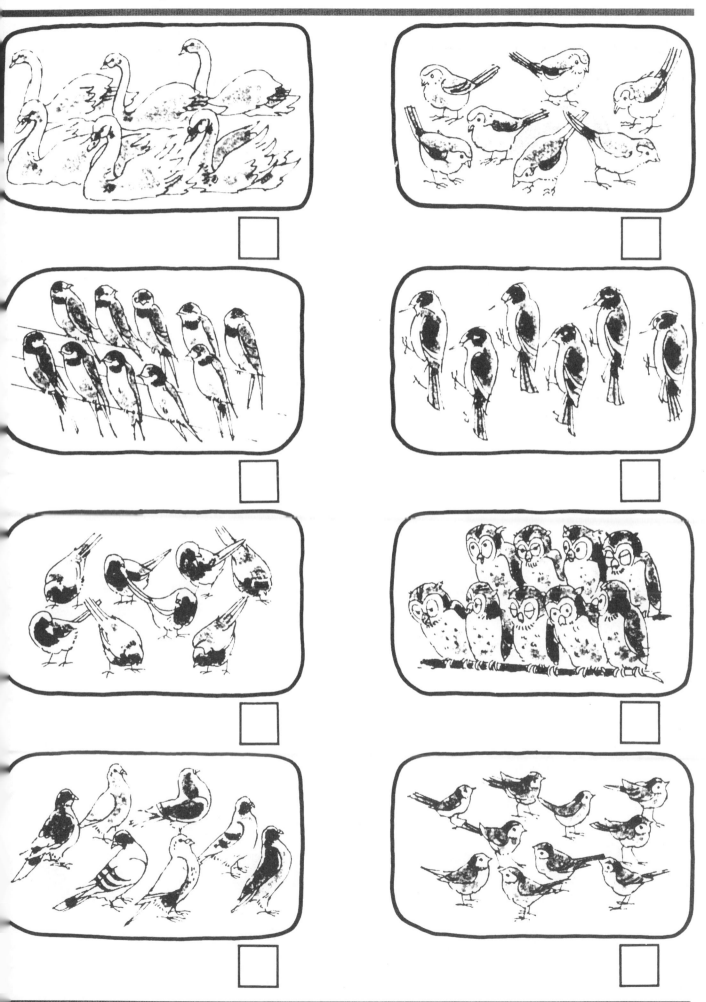

How many ?

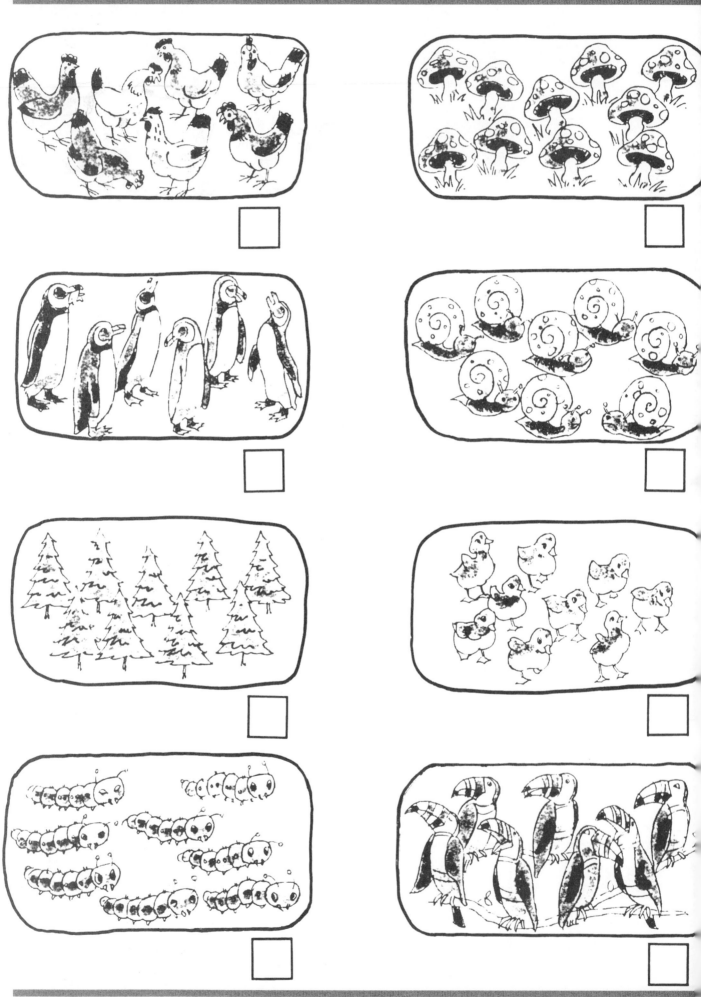

How many can you count?

Count and colour

Colour 4

Colour 7

Colour 10

Colour 6

Colour 8

Colour 9

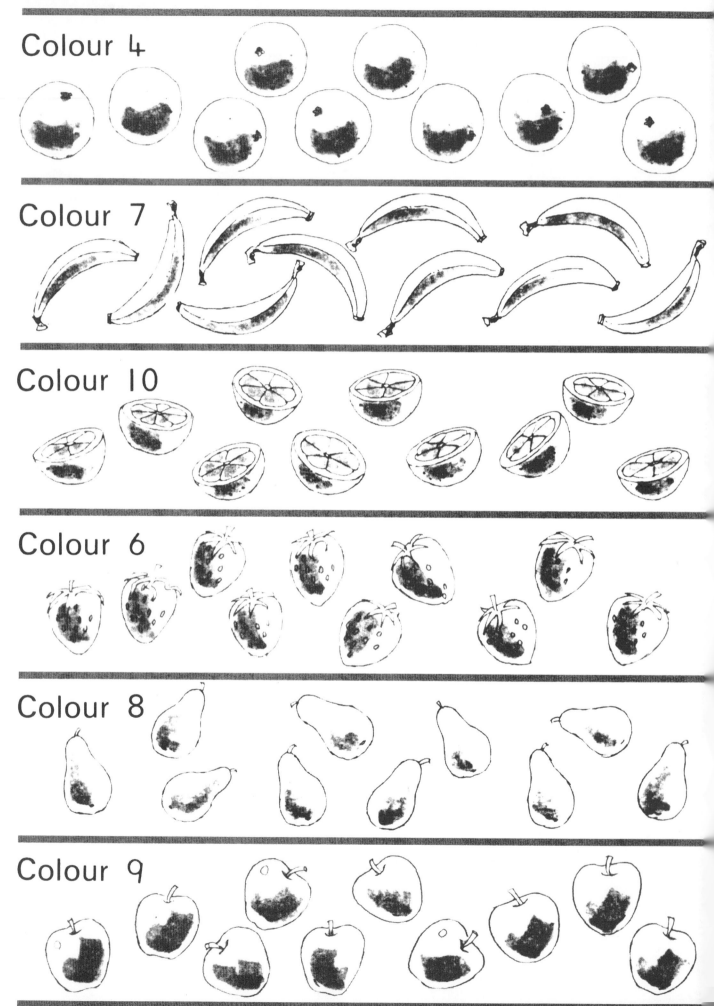

Draw and count

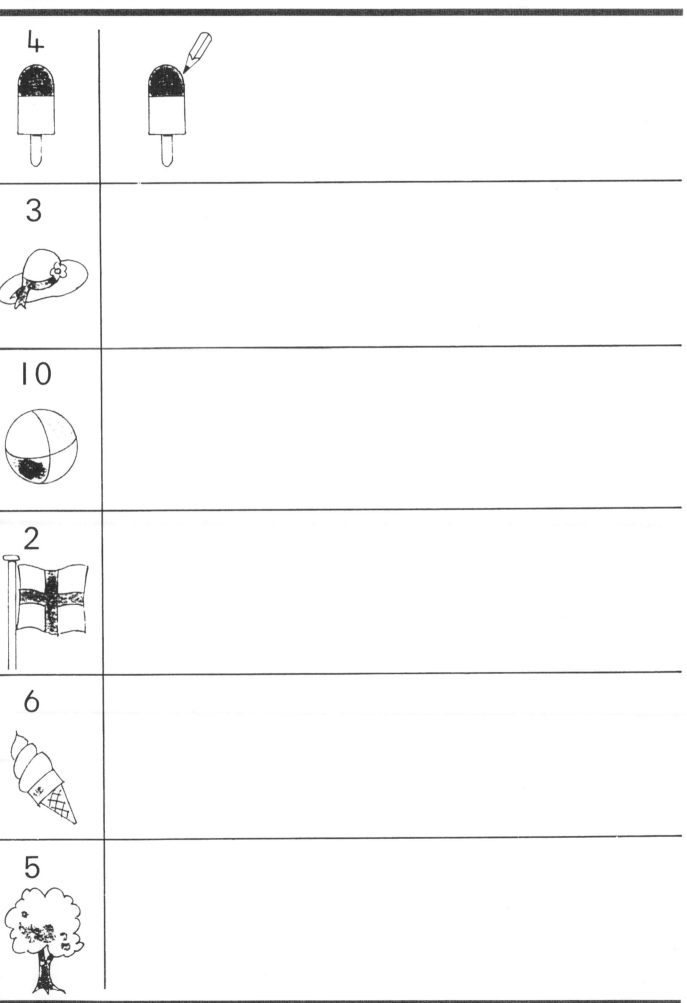

How much in each purse?

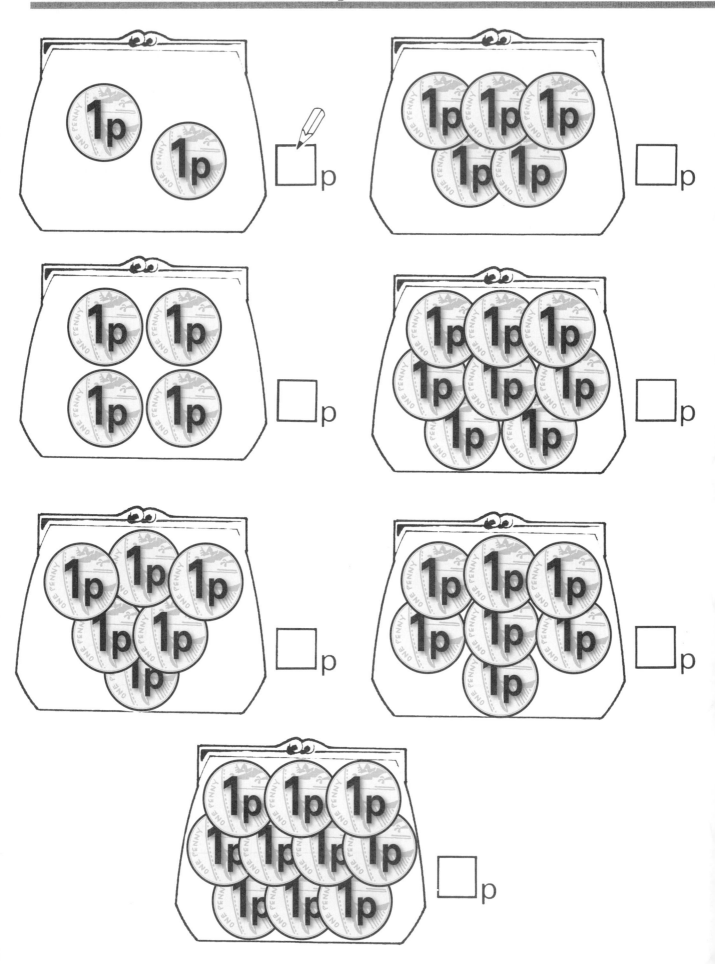

Draw lp coins in the purses

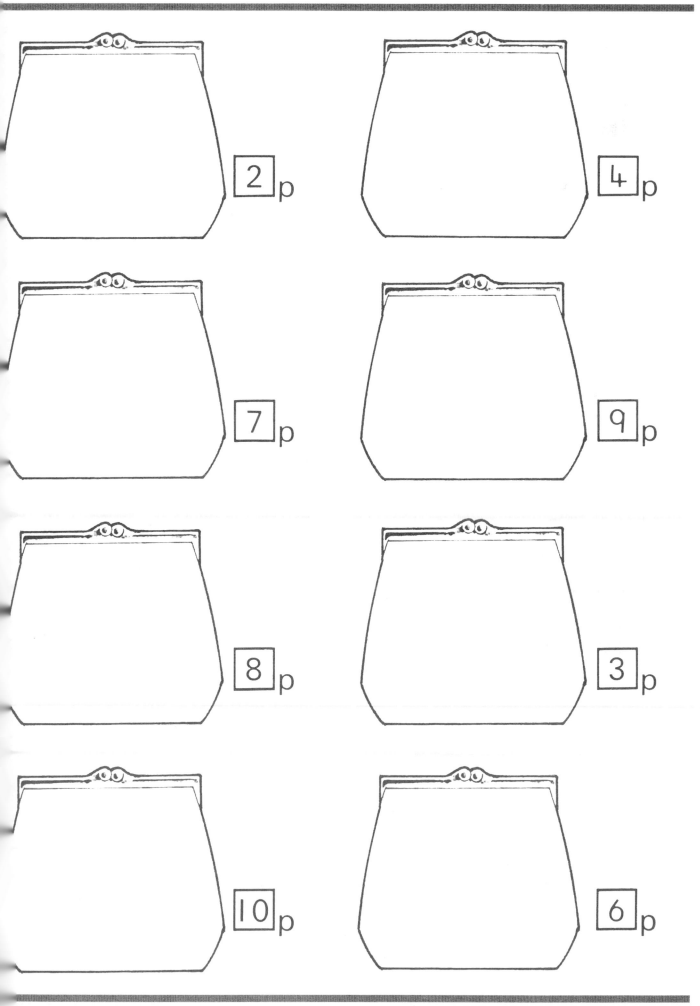

2 p

4 p

7 p

9 p

8 p

3 p

10 p

6 p

11

Adding 1

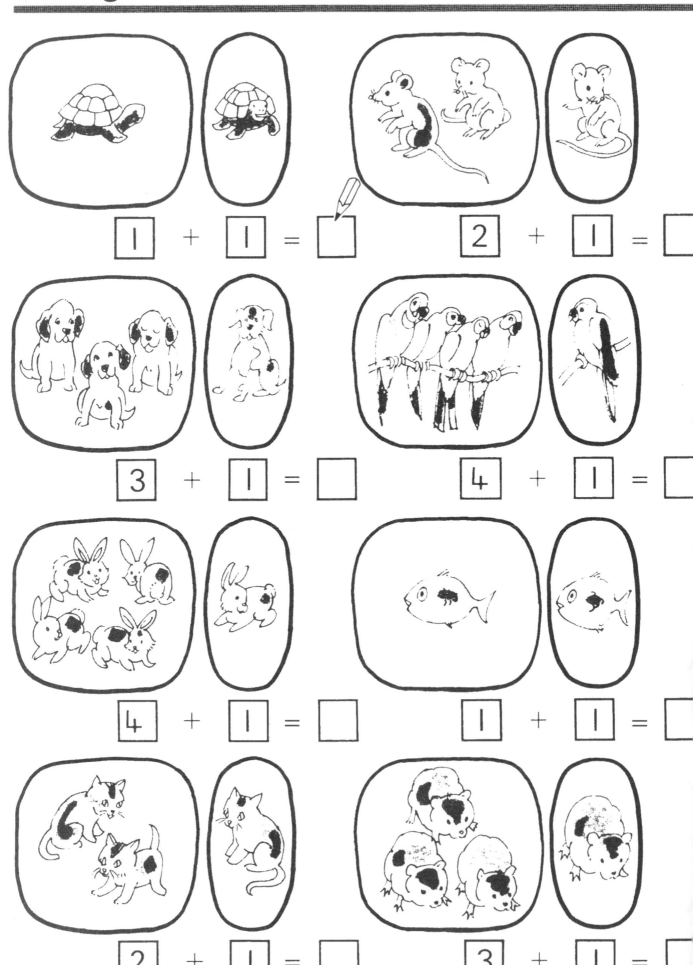

1 + 1 = ☐   2 + 1 = ☐

3 + 1 = ☐   4 + 1 = ☐

4 + 1 = ☐   1 + 1 = ☐

2 + 1 = ☐   3 + 1 = ☐

Adding 1

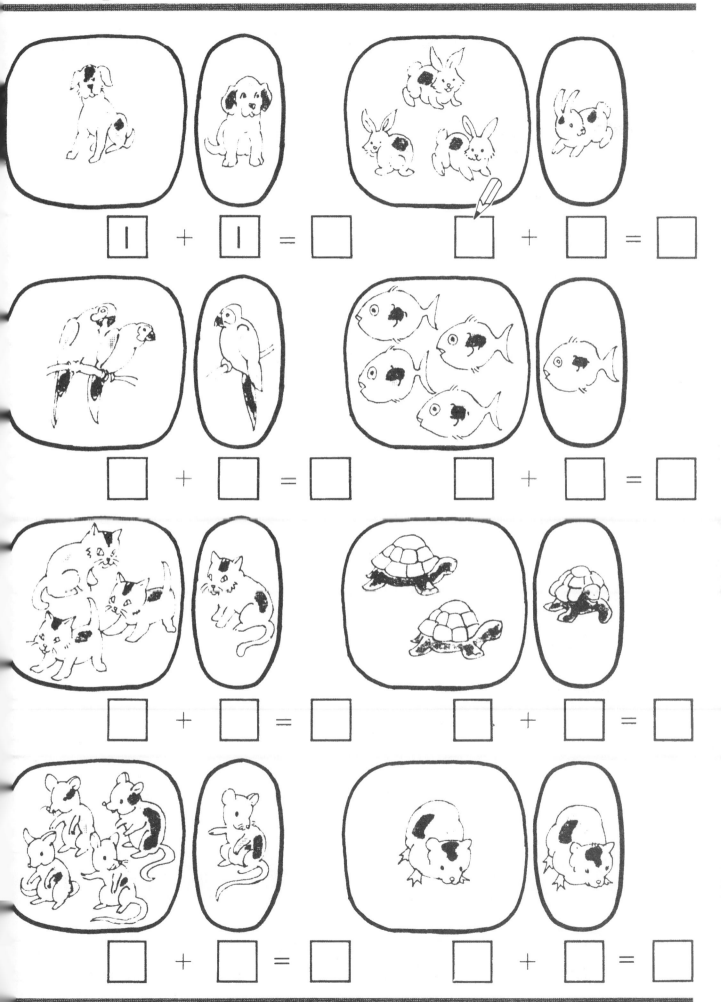

$\boxed{1}$ + $\boxed{1}$ = $\boxed{}$ $\boxed{}$ + $\boxed{}$ = $\boxed{}$

$\boxed{}$ + $\boxed{}$ = $\boxed{}$ $\boxed{}$ + $\boxed{}$ = $\boxed{}$

$\boxed{}$ + $\boxed{}$ = $\boxed{}$ $\boxed{}$ + $\boxed{}$ = $\boxed{}$

$\boxed{}$ + $\boxed{}$ = $\boxed{}$ $\boxed{}$ + $\boxed{}$ = $\boxed{}$

Adding 1

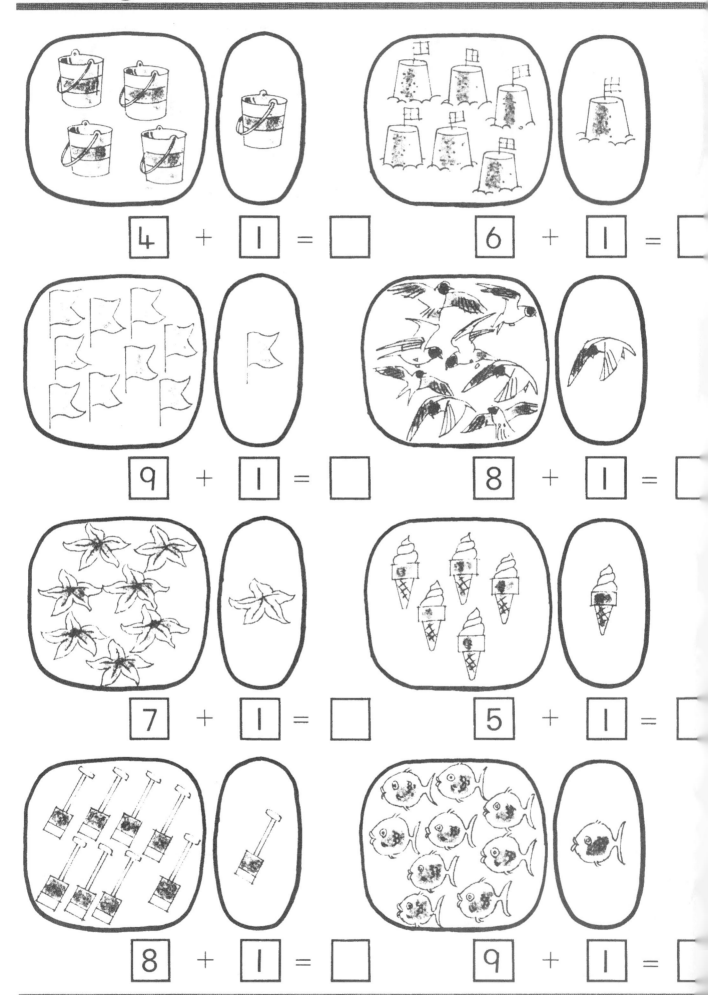

4 + 1 = ☐ 6 + 1 = ☐

9 + 1 = ☐ 8 + 1 = ☐

7 + 1 = ☐ 5 + 1 = ☐

8 + 1 = ☐ 9 + 1 = ☐

Adding I

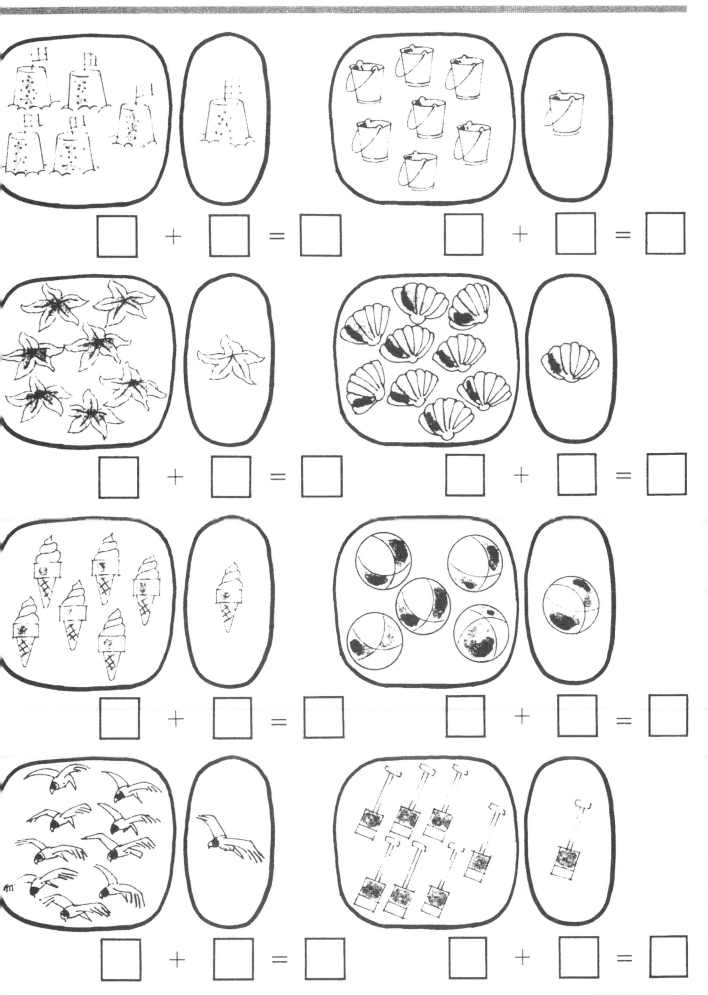

□ + □ = □   □ + □ = □

□ + □ = □   □ + □ = □

□ + □ = □   □ + □ = □

□ + □ = □   □ + □ = □

15

Adding 1

| 0 | 1 | 2 | 3 | 4 | 5 | 6 | 7 | 8 | 9 | 10 |

1 + 1 = ☐2☐   2 + 1 = ☐   3 + 1 = ☐

4 + 1 = ☐   5 + 1 = ☐   6 + 1 = ☐

7 + 1 = ☐   8 + 1 = ☐   9 + 1 = ☐

---

2 + 1 = ☐   4 + 1 = ☐   7 + 1 = ☐

6 + 1 = ☐   8 + 1 = ☐   5 + 1 = ☐

1 + 1 = ☐   9 + 1 = ☐   3 + 1 = ☐

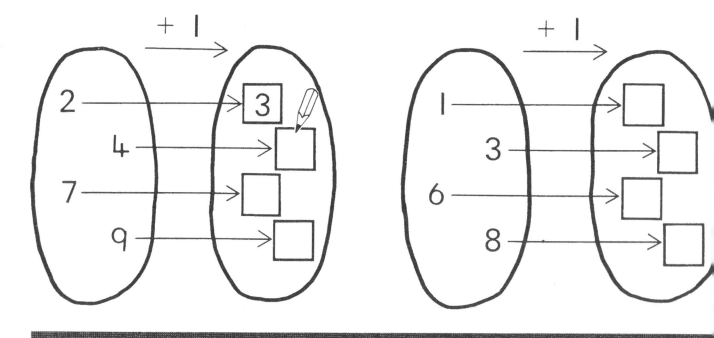

0   1   ☐   3   4   ☐   6   ☐   8   9   ☐

Adding 2

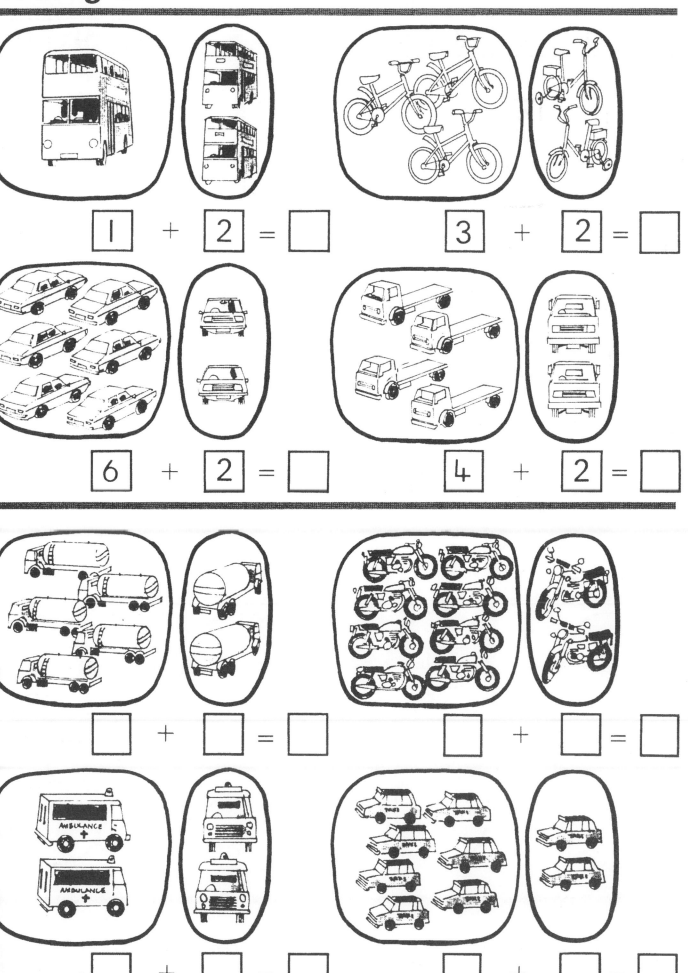

1 + 2 = ☐ 3 + 2 = ☐

6 + 2 = ☐ 4 + 2 = ☐

☐ + ☐ = ☐   ☐ + ☐ = ☐

☐ + ☐ = ☐   ☐ + ☐ = ☐

17

Adding 2

0	I	2	3	4	5	6	7	8	9	10

I + 2 = ☐   2 + 2 = ☐   3 + 2 = ☐

4 + 2 = ☐   5 + 2 = ☐   6 + 2 = ☐

7 + 2 = ☐   8 + 2 = ☐   5 + 2 = ☐

---

4 + 2 = ☐   6 + 2 = ☐   7 + 2 = ☐

8 + 2 = ☐   I + 2 = ☐   5 + 2 = ☐

3 + 2 = ☐   2 + 2 = ☐   8 + 2 = ☐

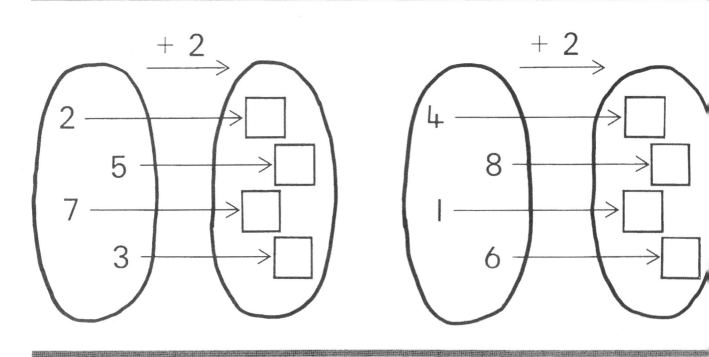

Adding 3

1 + 3 = ☐

3 + 3 = ☐

5 + 3 = ☐

4 + 3 = ☐

☐ + ☐ = ☐

☐ + ☐ = ☐

☐ + ☐ = ☐

☐ + ☐ = ☐

Adding 3

0	1	2	3	4	5	6	7	8	9	10

1 + 3 = ☐   2 + 3 = ☐   3 + 3 = ☐

4 + 3 = ☐   5 + 3 = ☐   6 + 3 = ☐

7 + 3 = ☐   4 + 3 = ☐   5 + 3 = ☐

---

5 + 3 = ☐   2 + 3 = ☐   7 + 3 = ☐

4 + 3 = ☐   1 + 3 = ☐   6 + 3 = ☐

7 + 3 = ☐   5 + 3 = ☐   3 + 3 = ☐

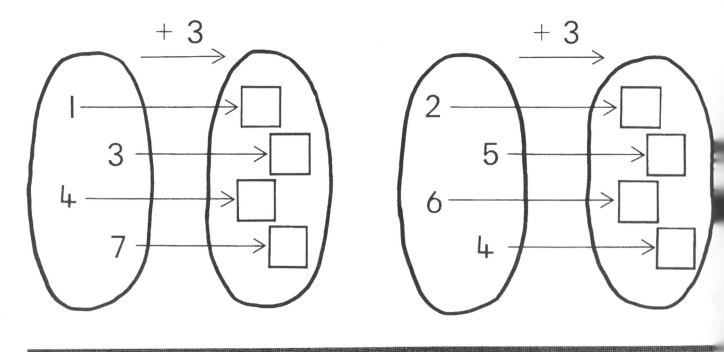

0	1	☐	☐	4	5	☐	☐	☐	9	☐

20

Adding 4

| 0 | 1 | 2 | 3 | 4 | 5 | 6 | 7 | 8 | 9 | 10 |

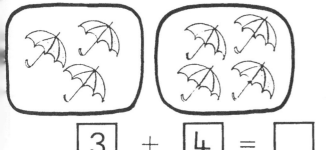 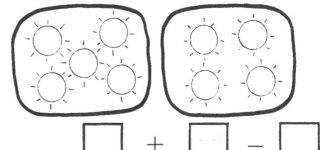

$\boxed{3}$ + $\boxed{4}$ = $\square$ $\square$ + $\square$ = $\square$

1 + 4 = $\square$ 2 + 4 = $\square$ 3 + 4 = $\square$

+ + 4 = $\square$ 5 + 4 = $\square$ 6 + 4 = $\square$

Adding 5

$\boxed{2}$ + $\boxed{5}$ = $\square$ $\square$ + $\square$ = $\square$

1 + 5 = $\square$ 2 + 5 = $\square$ 3 + 5 = $\square$

+ + 5 = $\square$ 5 + 5 = $\square$ 2 + 5 = $\square$

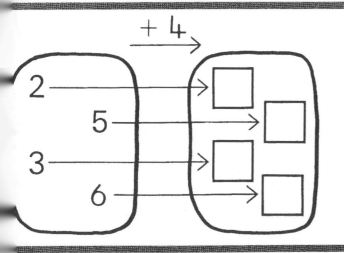 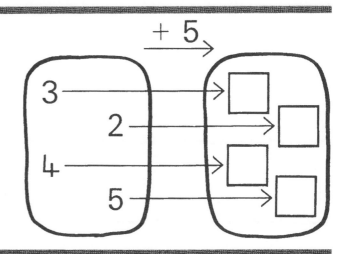

Adding

0	1	2	3	4	5	6	7	8	9	10

1 + 3 = ☐ 2 + 4 = ☐ 3 + 5 = ☐

5 + 2 = ☐ 4 + 4 = ☐ 6 + 4 = ☐

2 + 7 = ☐ 5 + 3 = ☐ 1 + 9 = ☐

---

2 + 6 = ☐ 3 + 2 = ☐ 1 + 8 = ☐

4 + 5 = ☐ 2 + 8 = ☐ 7 + 3 = ☐

2 + 5 = ☐ 5 + 1 = ☐ 3 + 6 = ☐

---

4 + 2 = ☐ 2 + 2 = ☐ 1 + 7 = ☐

5 + 5 = ☐ 8 + 2 = ☐ 6 + 3 = ☐

7 + 2 = ☐ 3 + 4 = ☐ 9 + 1 = ☐

---

8 + 1 = ☐ 4 + 6 = ☐ 2 + 3 = ☐

1 + 5 = ☐ 3 + 3 = ☐ 6 + 2 = ☐

5 + 4 = ☐ 2 + 1 = ☐ 7 + 1 = ☐

Shopping

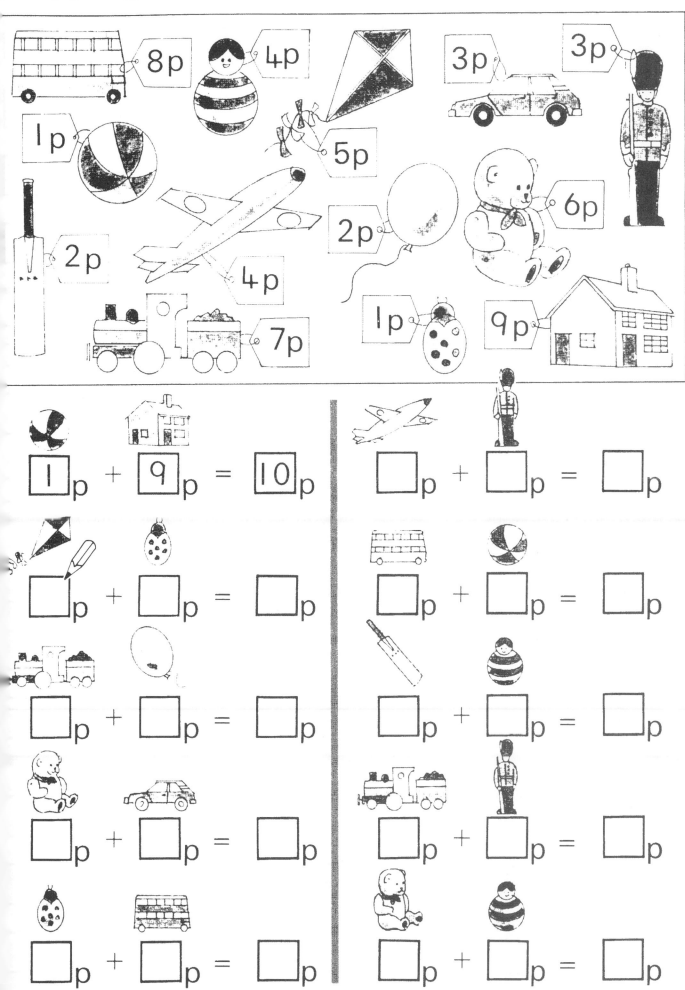

$\boxed{1}$ p $+$ $\boxed{9}$ p $=$ $\boxed{10}$ p

$\square$ p $+$ $\square$ p $=$ $\square$ p

$\square$ p $+$ $\square$ p $=$ $\square$ p

$\square$ p $+$ $\square$ p $=$ $\square$ p

$\square$ p $+$ $\square$ p $=$ $\square$ p

$\square$ p $+$ $\square$ p $=$ $\square$ p

$\square$ p $+$ $\square$ p $=$ $\square$ p

$\square$ p $+$ $\square$ p $=$ $\square$ p

$\square$ p $+$ $\square$ p $=$ $\square$ p

23

Taking away 1

10	9	8	7	6	5	4	3	2	1	0

1 − 1 = 0

2 − 1 = ☐

3 − 1 = ☐

4 − 1 = ☐

5 − 1 = ☐

6 − 1 = ☐

7 − 1 = ☐

8 − 1 = ☐

9 − 1 = ☐

4 − 1 = 3

2 − 1 = ☐

6 − 1 = ☐

1 − 1 = ☐

8 − 1 = ☐

3 − 1 = ☐

9 − 1 = ☐

5 − 1 = ☐

7 − 1 = ☐

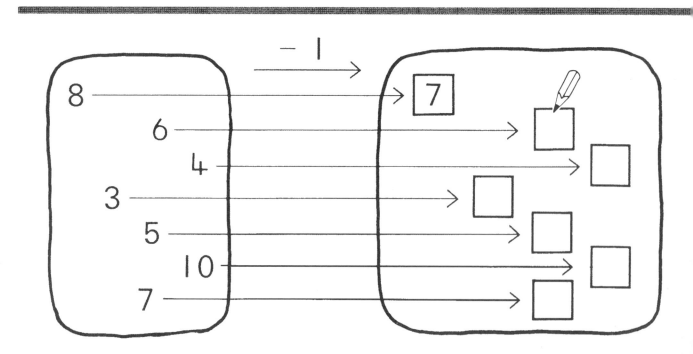

Taking away 2

2 – 2 = ☐   3 – 2 = ☐   4 – 2 = ☐

5 – 2 = ☐   6 – 2 = ☐   7 – 2 = ☐

8 – 2 = ☐   9 – 2 = ☐   10 – 2 = ☐

---

6 – 2 = ☐   2 – 2 = ☐   8 – 2 = ☐

10 – 2 = ☐   7 – 2 = ☐   3 – 2 = ☐

4 – 2 = ☐   9 – 2 = ☐   5 – 2 = ☐

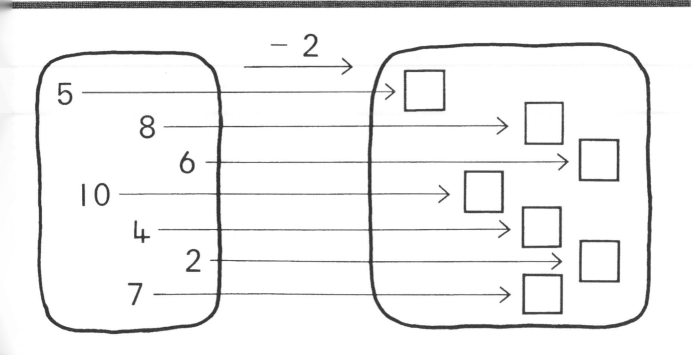

25

Taking away 3

10	9	8	7	6	5	4	3	2	1	0

3 – 3 = ☐   4 – 3 = ☐   5 – 3 = ☐

6 – 3 = ☐   7 – 3 = ☐   8 – 3 = ☐

9 – 3 = ☐   10 – 3 = ☐

---

4 – 3 = ☐   6 – 3 = ☐   9 – 3 = ☐

8 – 3 = ☐   3 – 3 = ☐   5 – 3 = ☐

7 – 3 = ☐   10 – 3 = ☐   8 – 3 = ☐

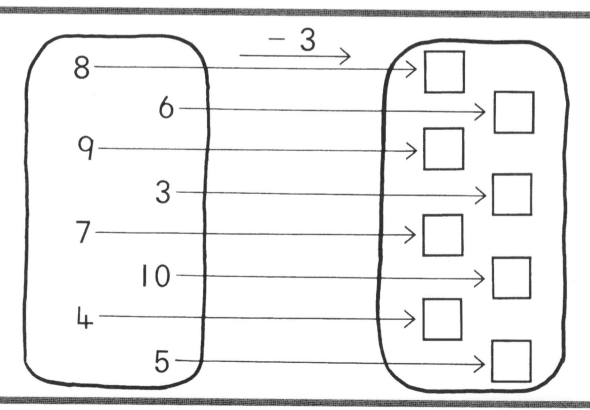

Taking away 4

10	9	8	7	6	5	4	3	2	1	0

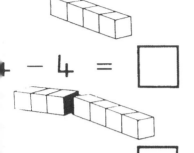

4 − 4 = ☐

5 − 4 = ☐

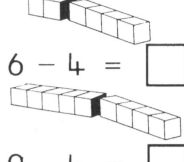

6 − 4 = ☐

7 − 4 = ☐

8 − 4 = ☐

9 − 4 = ☐

10 − 4 = ☐

---

6 − 4 = ☐   9 − 4 = ☐   4 − 4 = ☐

3 − 4 = ☐   5 − 4 = ☐   10 − 4 = ☐

9 − 4 = ☐   7 − 4 = ☐   6 − 4 = ☐

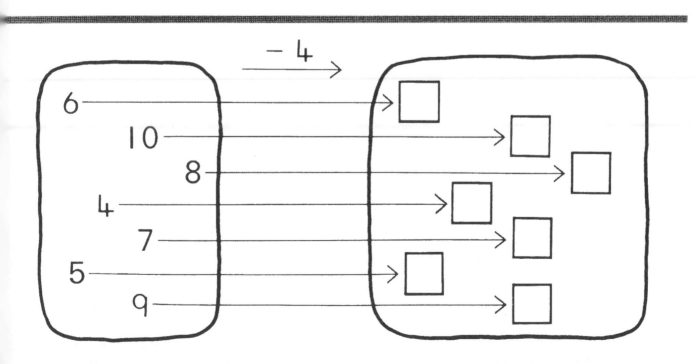

Taking away 5

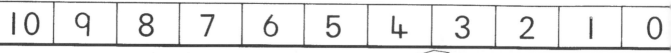

10	9	8	7	6	5	4	3	2	1	0

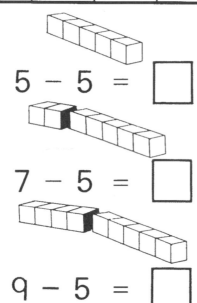

$5 - 5 = \square$

$6 - 5 = \square$

$7 - 5 = \square$

$8 - 5 = \square$

$9 - 5 = \square$

$10 - 5 = \square$

$7 - 5 = \square$ $10 - 5 = \square$ $5 - 5 = \square$

$9 - 5 = \square$ $6 - 5 = \square$ $8 - 5 = \square$

$5 - 5 = \square$ $7 - 5 = \square$ $10 - 5 = \square$

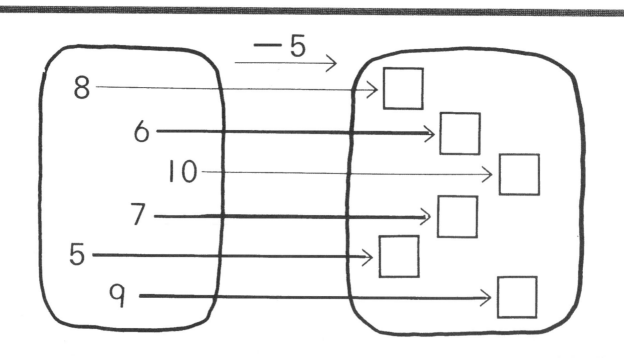

Taking away 6

10	9	8	7	6	5	4	3	2	1	0

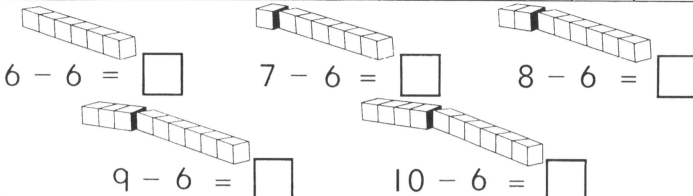

$6 - 6 = \boxed{}$ $7 - 6 = \boxed{}$ $8 - 6 = \boxed{}$

$9 - 6 = \boxed{}$ $10 - 6 = \boxed{}$

$8 - 6 = \boxed{}$ $10 - 6 = \boxed{}$ $7 - 6 = \boxed{}$

$10 - 6 = \boxed{}$ $6 - 6 = \boxed{}$ $9 - 6 = \boxed{}$

Taking away 7

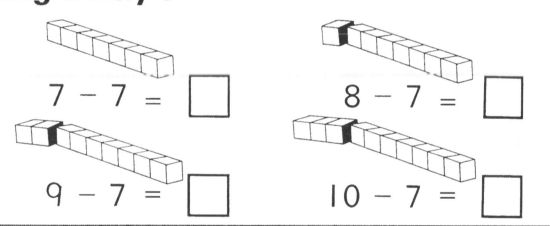

$7 - 7 = \boxed{}$ $8 - 7 = \boxed{}$

$9 - 7 = \boxed{}$ $10 - 7 = \boxed{}$

$9 - 7 = \boxed{}$ $7 - 7 = \boxed{}$ $10 - 7 = \boxed{}$

$0 - 7 = \boxed{}$ $8 - 7 = \boxed{}$ $9 - 7 = \boxed{}$

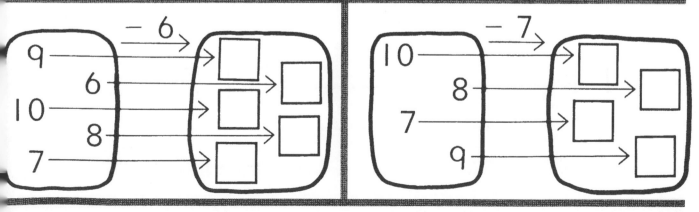

Shopping

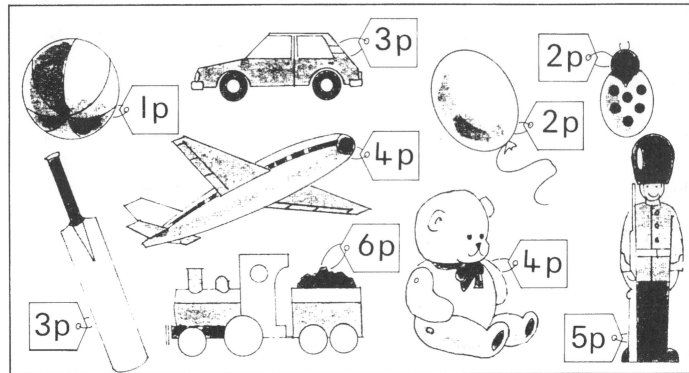

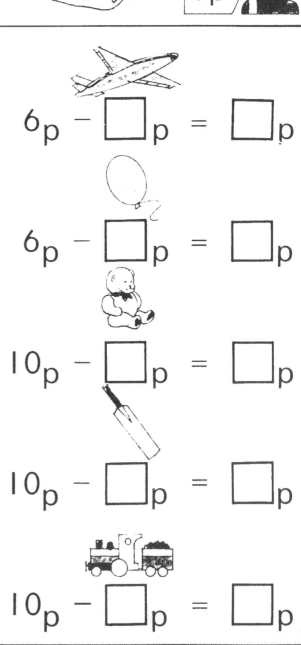

$5_p - \boxed{2}_p = \boxed{3}_p$

$6_p - \boxed{}_p = \boxed{}_p$

$5_p - \boxed{}_p = \boxed{}_p$

$6_p - \boxed{}_p = \boxed{}_p$

$8_p - \boxed{}_p = \boxed{}_p$

$10_p - \boxed{}_p = \boxed{}_p$

$8_p - \boxed{}_p = \boxed{}_p$

$10_p - \boxed{}_p = \boxed{}_p$

$8_p - \boxed{}_p = \boxed{}_p$

$10_p - \boxed{}_p = \boxed{}_p$

aking away

3 − 1 = ☐   5 − 1 = ☐   6 − 1 = ☐

9 − 1 = ☐   4 − 2 = ☐   7 − 3 = ☐

+ − 4 = ☐   7 − 4 = ☐   6 − 5 = ☐

3 − 6 = ☐   10 − 5 = ☐   9 − 2 = ☐

---

3 − 2 = ☐   5 − 3 = ☐   7 − 1 = ☐

0 − 3 = ☐   8 − 4 = ☐   6 − 2 = ☐

+ − 1 = ☐   3 − 3 = ☐   9 − 0 = ☐

---

2 − 2 = ☐   7 − 2 = ☐   3 − 3 = ☐

5 − 4 = ☐   8 − 5 = ☐   6 − 6 = ☐

1 − 0 = ☐   10 − 2 = ☐   8 − 1 = ☐

---

7 − 5 = ☐   9 − 2 = ☐   10 − 10 = ☐

9 − 4 = ☐   6 − 0 = ☐   5 − 2 = ☐

3 − 3 = ☐   7 − 6 = ☐   10 − 7 = ☐

Schofield&Sims

the long-established educational publisher
specialising in maths, English and science materials for schools

Number Book is a series of graded activity books helping children to learn basic calculation skills, including·addition, subtraction, multiplication and division.

Number Book 1 includes:

- Counting sets of objects to 10
- Addition to 10
- Subtraction from 10.

This book is suitable for children making the transition from the Early Years Foundation Stage to Key Stage 1 and those already in Key Stage 1.

The full range of titles in the series is as follows:

Number Book 1:   ISBN 978 07217 0788 4

Number Book 2:   ISBN 978 07217 0789 1

Number Book 3:   ISBN 978 07217 0790 7

Number Book 4:   ISBN 978 07217 0791 4

Number Book 5:   ISBN 978 07217 0792 1

Have you tried **Problem Solving** by Schofield & Sims?
This series helps children to sharpen their mathematical skills by applying their knowledge to a range of number problems and 'real-life' contexts.

For further information and to place your order
visit www.schofieldandsims.co.uk or telephone 01484 607080

ISBN 978 07217 0788 4

£2.45
(Retail price)

Key Stage 1
Age range: 5–7 years
(Books at either end of the series incorporate some overlap with earlier and later key stages to support transition)

ISBN 978-07217-0788-4

9 780721 707884

Schofield&Sims

Dogley Mill, Fenay Bridge, Huddersfield HD8 0NQ
Phone: 01484 607080 Facsimile: 01484 606815
E-mail: sales@schofieldandsims.co.uk